SCHOLASTIC

Do The Math™

Created by
Marilyn Burns

 # Addition & Subtraction (A)

Addition with sums up to 100

. . . .

WorkSpace

Adrian

Cover: © Photodisc Photography/Veer, insets top: © Pamela Burley/iStockphoto.com, tc: © John Meyer/iStockPhotos.com.

Copyright © 2008 by Scholastic Inc.

All rights reserved.   Published by Scholastic Inc.   Printed in the U.S.A.

ISBN-13: 978-0-545-00978-2
ISBN-10: 0-545-00978-2

13 14 15   40   16 15 14 13

v.B

Write Addition Equations

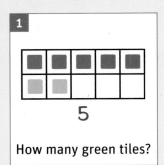

1 5

How many green tiles?

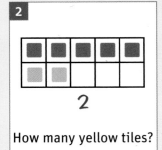

2 2

How many yellow tiles?

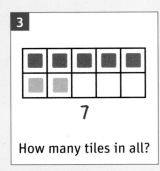

3 7

How many tiles in all?

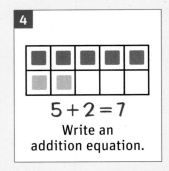

4 $5 + 2 = 7$

Write an addition equation.

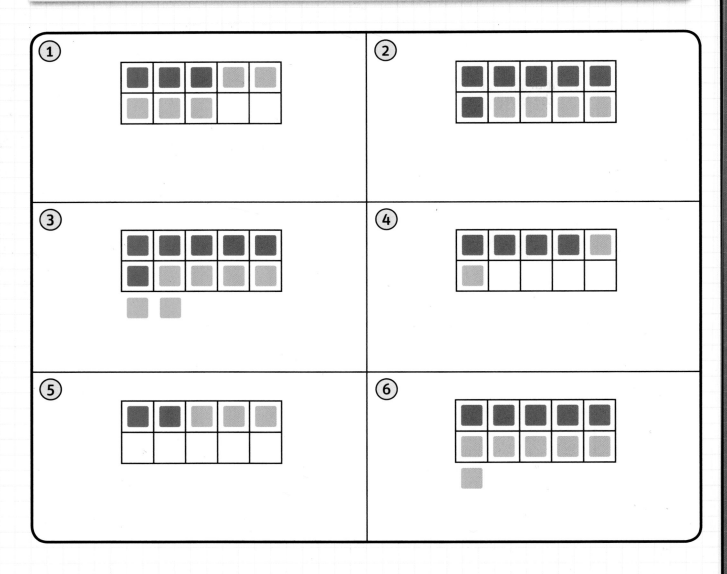

①

②

③

④

⑤

⑥

Lesson 2

Home Note: Your child writes equations to match the green and yellow tiles shown, adding two numbers from 1 to 6.

Game Rules for Which Sum Wins?

What you need

- (1–6) number cube
- ten-frame
- tiles
- *WorkSpace* page 4 or 9
- pencil

➤ **Players take turns. Each turn has four steps.**

1

Roll the cube. Put that number of green tiles on the ten-frame.

2

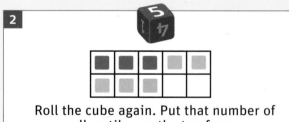

Roll the cube again. Put that number of yellow tiles on the ten-frame.

3

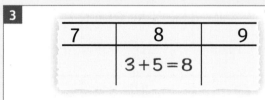

7	8	9
	3 + 5 = 8	

Write the equation under the correct sum on the *WorkSpace* page.

4

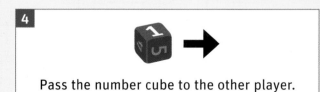

Pass the number cube to the other player.

➤ **The winner is the first player to fill all the spaces under one sum.**

Home Note: Your child uses these rules to play an addition game in which he or she has practice adding two numbers from 1 to 6.

Which Sum Wins?

HOW TO PLAY

> Players take turns. Each turn has four steps.

1. Roll the cube. Put that number of green tiles on the ten-frame.

2. Roll the cube again. Put that number of yellow tiles on the ten-frame.

3. Write the equation under the correct sum.

7	8	9
	$3+5=8$	

4. Pass the number cube to the other player.

> The winner is the first player to fill all the spaces under one sum.

Sums:

2	3	4	5	6

7	8	9	10	11	12

Lesson 2

Home Note: Your child writes addition equations.

Write Addition Equations

1
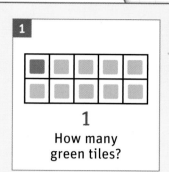
1
How many
green tiles?

2
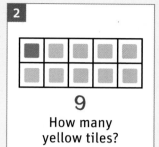
9
How many
yellow tiles?

3
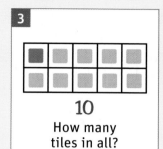
10
How many
tiles in all?

4
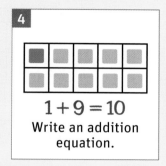
$1 + 9 = 10$
Write an addition
equation.

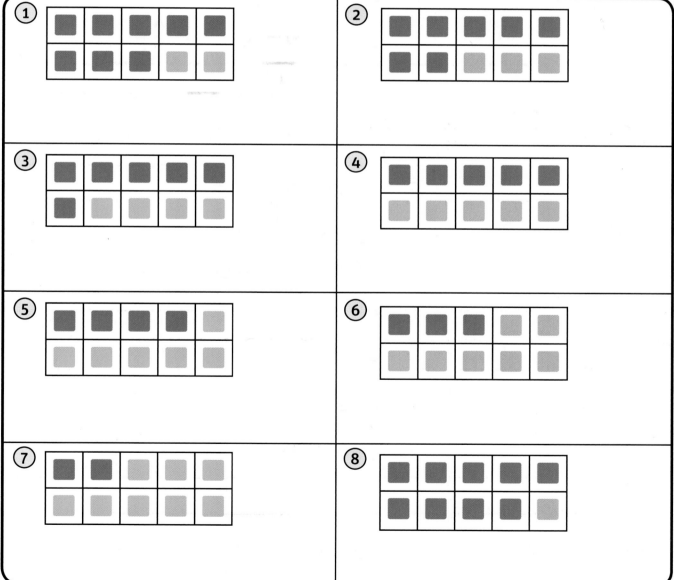

Home Note: Your child shows combinations of addends
that have a sum of 10, and writes the matching equations.

Sums of Ten

1 Use a ten-frame and tiles to find three or more numbers that add up to 10.

2 $2 + 2 + 3 + 3 = 10$

Write an addition equation.

$2 + 2 + 3 + 3 = 10$

Home Note: Your child writes as many equations as possible that show a sum of 10. Each equation shows more than two numbers being added.

Show What You Know

1

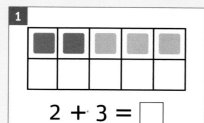

$2 + 3 = \square$

Place tiles on a ten-frame to match the numbers.

2

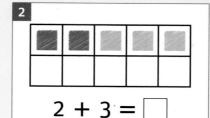

$2 + 3 = \square$

Color the boxes to match your ten-frame.

3

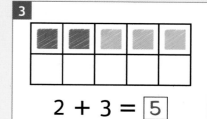

$2 + 3 = \boxed{5}$

Write the sum.

---

①

$6 + 2 + 2 = \boxed{10}$

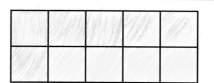

②

$5 + 6 = \boxed{11}$

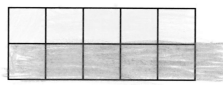

③

$4 + 4 + 1 = \square$

④

$7 + 2 = \square$

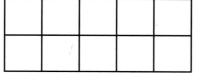

⑤

$5 + 2 + 3 = \square$

Home Note: Your child fills boxes in ten-frames to show the numbers in equations, and then writes the sums of the equations.

Show What You Know

1

We invited 2 dogs
and 3 cats.
How many
came to tea?

Read the problem.

2

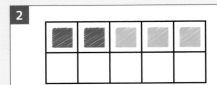

Color the ten-frame
to match the problem.

3

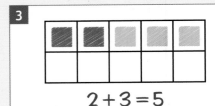

$2 + 3 = 5$

Write an addition equation.

---

1 We invited 4 clowns and 3 mice.
How many came to tea?

$4 + 3 = 7$

---

2 We invited 5 birds, 3 cats, and 2 dogs.
How many came to tea?

$5 + 3 + 2 = 10$

---

3 We invited 8 drummers and 3 painters.
How many came to tea?

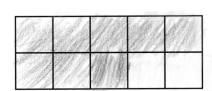

$8 + 3 = 11$

Home Note: Your child fills in ten-frames to show the numbers
in word problems, and writes equations to match the problems.

Which Sum Wins?

HOW TO PLAY

➤ **Players take turns. Each turn has four steps.**

1 Roll the cube.
Put that number of green tiles on the ten-frame.

2 Roll the cube again.
Put that number of yellow tiles on the ten-frame.

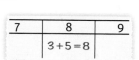

3

7	8	9
	3+5=8	

Write the equation under the correct sum.

4 Pass the number cube to the other player.

➤ **The winner is the first player to fill all the spaces under one sum.**

Sums:

2	3	4	5	6
1+1=2			1+4=5	

7	8	9	10	11	12
		5+4=9		5+6=11	
				5+6=11	
				5+6=11	

Home Note: Your child writes addition equations.

Game Rules for Seven-Up

What you need

• number cards, four of each number 1–10

➤ **Partners play the game cooperatively.**

1

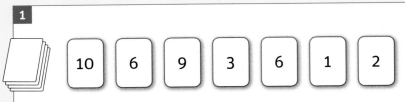

| 10 | 6 | 9 | 3 | 6 | 1 | 2 |

Turn seven cards face up.
Leave the rest face down in a pile.

2

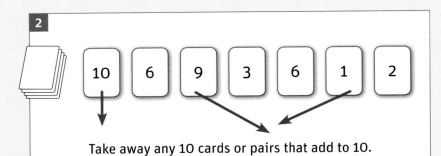

| 10 | 6 | 9 | 3 | 6 | 1 | 2 |

Take away any 10 cards or pairs that add to 10.

3

| 2 | 6 | 1 | 3 | 6 | 5 | 2 |

Keep seven cards face up with new cards from the pack.

4

| 3 | 7 | 9 | 8 | 1 | 4 | 6 |

When there are no 10s, put a new row on top.

➤ **Play until you can no longer find or make tens or you have used up all the cards.**

Home Note: Your child practices finding pairs of numbers with sums of 10 by playing a game.

Game Rules for The Spillover Game

What you need

- number cube (4–9)
- number cube (6–10)
- green and yellow crayons
- *WorkSpace* pages 12, 13, or 17

➤ **Players take turns. Each turn has four steps.**

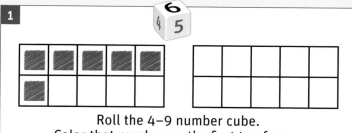

1

Roll the 4–9 number cube.
Color that number on the first ten-frame.

2

Roll the 6–10 number cube.
Color that number on the ten-frames.

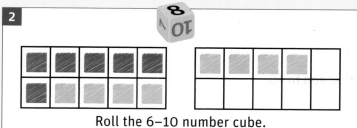

3

Equations: $6 + 8 = 14$ Spillover: 4
$10 + 4 = 14$

Write the equations and your spillover.

4

Pass the number cubes to your partner.

➤ **After both players finish their turns, draw a star next to the greater spillover.**

➤ **After five turns each, the player with more stars is the winner.**

Home Note: Your child practices adding pairs of numbers by playing a game.

The Spillover Game

Player A	Player B

EXAMPLE

Player A:
Equations: $5 + 7 = 12$ Spillover: 2
$10 + 2 = 12$ ☆

Player B:
Equations: $4 + 6 = 10$ Spillover: 0
$10 + 0 = 10$

Player A — Equations: _____   Spillover: _____

Player B — Equations: _____   Spillover: _____

Player A — Equations: _____   Spillover: _____

Player B — Equations: _____   Spillover: _____

Player A — Equations: _____   Spillover: _____

Player B — Equations: _____   Spillover: _____

Player A — Equations: _____   Spillover: _____

Player B — Equations: _____   Spillover: _____

Player A — Equations: _____   Spillover: _____

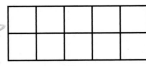
Player B — Equations: _____   Spillover: _____

Home Note: Your child practices adding pairs of numbers by playing a game.

The Spillover Game

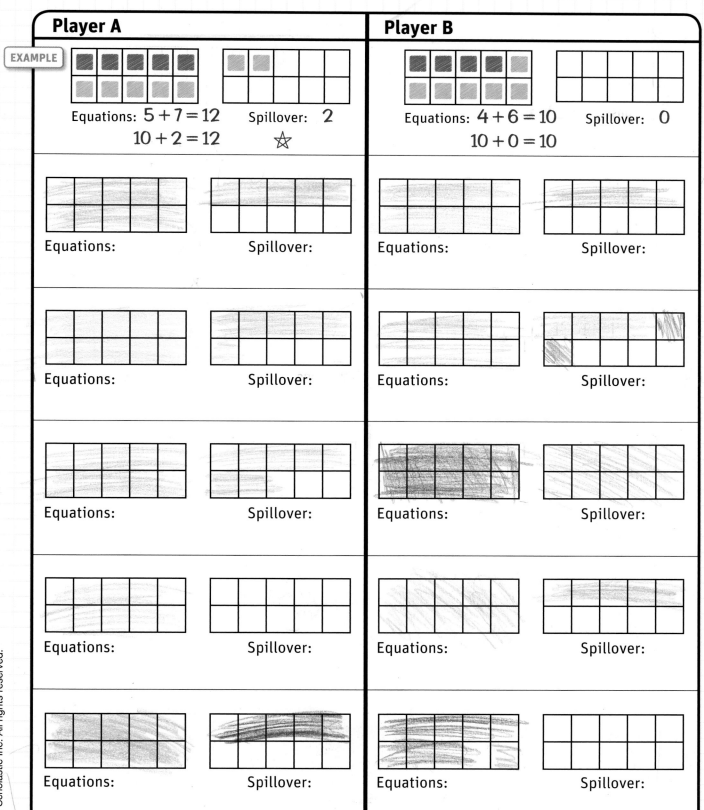

Player A	Player B
EXAMPLE	
Equations: $5 + 7 = 12$ Spillover: 2	Equations: $4 + 6 = 10$ Spillover: 0
$10 + 2 = 12$ ☆	$10 + 0 = 10$
Equations: Spillover:	Equations: Spillover:
Equations: Spillover:	Equations: Spillover:
Equations: Spillover:	Equations: Spillover:
Equations: Spillover:	Equations: Spillover:
Equations: Spillover:	Equations: Spillover:

Home Note: Your child practices adding pairs of numbers by playing a game.

Solve Addition Word Problems

DIRECTIONS

1

There are 4 frogs.
There are 9 bears.
How many friends
are there in all?

Read the problem.

2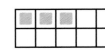

Color the ten-frames
to match the problem.

3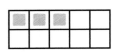

$$4 + 9 = 13$$
$$10 + 3 = 13$$
Write two addition equations.

---

① There are 3 drummers.
There are 9 bears.
How many friends are there in all?

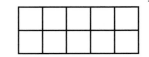

② There are 6 ballerinas.
There are 8 tailors.
How many friends are there in all?

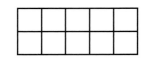

③ There are 9 bears.
There are 7 sailors.
How many friends are there in all?

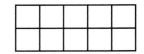

④ There are 8 tailors.
There are 5 sheep.
How many friends are there in all?

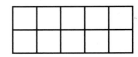

⑤ There are 7 sailors.
There are 6 ballerinas.
How many friends are there in all?

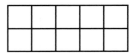 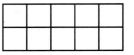 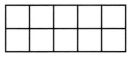 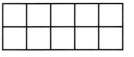 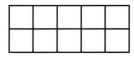 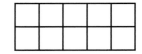

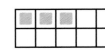 **Home Note:** Your child uses ten-frames to model word
problems, and writes two equations for each sum.

Add Numbers with Sums Greater than 10

DIRECTIONS

1

9, 7

Decide which number to add on to and which to split.

2

Take 1 from the 7 to make 10. The spillover is 6.

Think how to add by thinking of 10 plus a spillover.

3

$9 + 7 = 16$
$9 + 1 + 6 = 16$
$10 + 6 = 16$

Write equations.

① 5, 8

② 6, 5

③ 9, 6

④ 8, 6

⑤ 3, 8

⑥ 9, 8

Home Note: Your child adds two numbers with a sum greater than 10, explains how to find the sum, and writes equations showing the sum.

Show What You Know

➤ List each pair of cards that add to 10.

1 | 8 | 3 | 6 | 2 | 5 | 7 | 1

_____

➤ Write two equations for each pair of ten-frames.

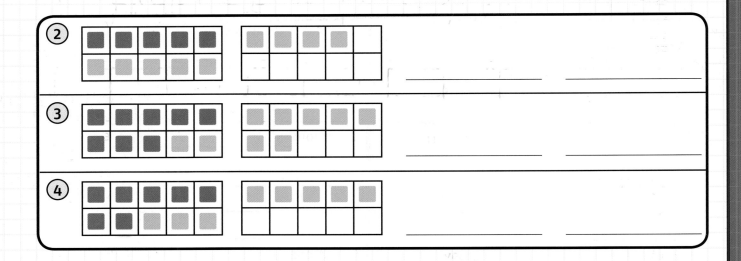

2 _____ _____

3 _____ _____

4 _____ _____

➤ Solve the word problem.
➤ Color the ten-frames to show the problem.
➤ Write two equations for the problem.

5 There are 7 sailors.
There are 5 sheep.
How many friends are there in all? _____

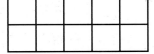 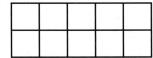

_____ _____

Home Note: Your child identifies pairs of numbers that add to 10, writes equations for sums greater than 10, and solves a word problem.

The Spillover Game

➤ See the rules on page 11.

Player A

EXAMPLE

Equations: $5 + 7 = 12$ Spillover: 2
$10 + 2 = 12$ ☆

Equations: Spillover:

Equations: Spillover:

Equations: Spillover:

Equations: Spillover:

Equations: Spillover:

Player B

Equations: $4 + 6 = 10$ Spillover: 0
$10 + 0 = 10$

Equations: Spillover:

Equations: Spillover:

Equations: Spillover:

Equations: Spillover:

Equations: Spillover:

Home Note: Your child practices adding pairs of numbers by playing a game.

Stars in One Minute

1

Draw one star in each square.
Draw for one minute.

2 There are ___6___ tens
and ___8___ ones.

Count and record the
tens and ones.

3 ___60___ + ___8___ = ___68___
So there are ___68___ stars.

Complete the equation
and write the total.

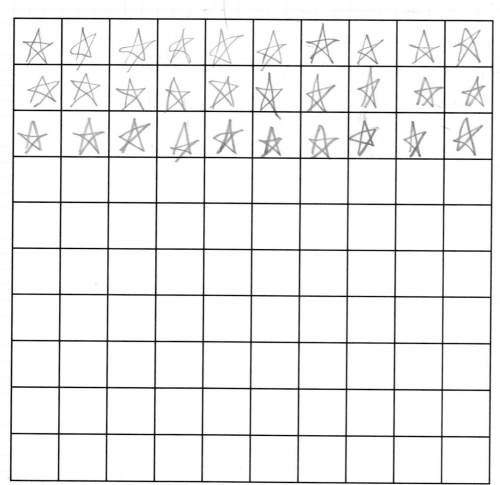

There are ___30___ tens and ___0___ ones.

___30___ + ___0___ = ___30___

So there are ___30___ stars.

Home Note: Your child uses a hundred-frame to count by tens and ones.

Tom Counts More

1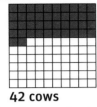

42 cows
Color the hundred grid
to show the number.

2
___4___ tens and ___2___ ones.

Write the tens and ones.

3
___40 + 2 = 42___

Write the equation.

---

(1)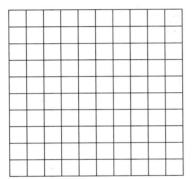

17 wasps

_____ tens and _____ ones

_____

(2)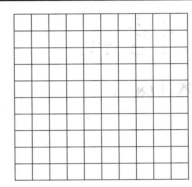

22 parrots

_____ tens and _____ ones

_____

(3)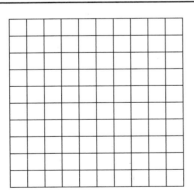

34 chickens

_____ tens and _____ ones

_____

(4)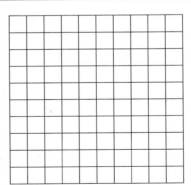

49 sharks

_____ tens and _____ ones

_____

Home Note: Your child uses hundred grids to show
two-digit numbers as sums of tens and ones.

⑤ 10
20
30
40
50

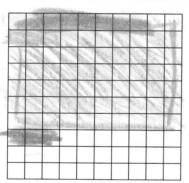

58 raccoons

_____5_____ tens and _____8_____ ones

58

$50 + 8 = 58$

⑥

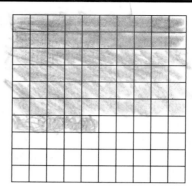

65 pigs

_____6_____ tens and _____ ones

$60 + 5 = 65$

⑦

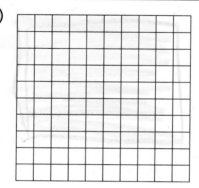

73 robots

_____7_____ tens and _____3_____ ones

$70 + 3 = 73$

⑧

80 apples

_____ tens and _____ ones

$80 + 0 = 80$

⑨

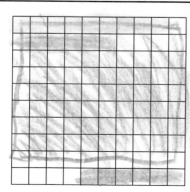

96 clouds

_____ tens and _____6_____ ones

$90 + 6 = 90$

Home Note: Your child uses hundred grids to show
two-digit numbers as sums of tens and ones.

Add 10

1

Tom counted 17 horses.
There are 10 more.
How many horses are
there in all?

Read the word problem.

2

Color the hundred grid
to show the addition.

3

$17 + 10 = \underline{27}$

$17 + \underline{3} = 20$

$20 + \underline{7} = 27$

Complete the equations.

1

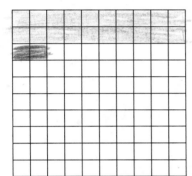

Tom counted 12 wolves.
There are 10 more.
How many wolves are there in all?

$12 + 10 = \underline{22}$

$12 + \underline{18} = 20$

$20 + \underline{12} = 22$

2

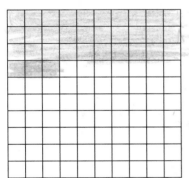

Tom counted 23 pythons.
There are 10 more.
How many pythons are there in all?

$23 + 10 = \underline{30}$

$23 + \underline{10} = 30$

$30 + \underline{3} = 33$

3

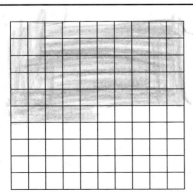

Tom counted 45 pirates.
There are 10 more.
How many pirates are there in all?

$45 + 10 = \underline{50}$

$45 + \underline{10} = 50$

$50 + \underline{5} = 55$

Home Note: Your child solves word problems by using a hundred grid.

1 to 100 Chart

➤ Complete the chart as your teacher directs.
➤ Write the numbers 1 through 10 in the chart.
➤ Write all the numbers that end with zero.
➤ Write the numbers 11, 21, 31, 41, and 51.
➤ Write all the other numbers.

1	2	3	4	5	6	7	8	9	10
11	12	13	14	15	16	17	18	19	20
21	22	23	24	25	26	27	28	29	30
31	32	33	34	35	36	37	38	39	40
41	42	43	44	45	46	47	48	49	50
51	52	53	54	55	56	57	58	59	60
61	62	63	64	65	66	67	68	69	70
71	72	73	74	75	76	77	78	79	80
81	82	83	84	85	86	87	88	89	90
91	92	93	94	95	96	97	98	99	100

Home Note: Your child writes the numbers 1–100 on a 1 to 100 chart.

Show What You Know

DIRECTIONS

➤ Read the word problem.
➤ Color the hundred grid to show the addition.
➤ Complete the equations.

①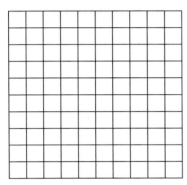

Tom counted 36 goats.
There were 10 more.
How many were there in all?

$36 + 10 =$ _____

$36 +$ _____ $= 40$

$40 + 6 =$ _____

②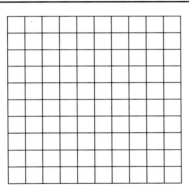

Tom counted 45 pirates.
There were 10 more.
How many were there in all?

$45 + 10 =$ _____

$45 +$ _____ $= 50$

$50 + 5 =$ _____

DIRECTIONS

➤ Shade the number on the grid. Write tens and ones and an equation.

③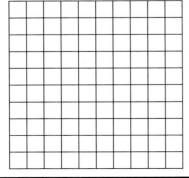

73 ducks

_____ tens and _____ ones

Equation _____

Home Note: Your child uses a hundred
grid to add 10 to a two-digit number.

Lesson 15

23

Show What You Know

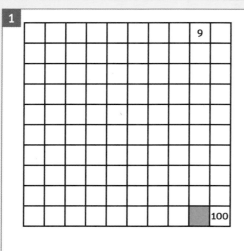

1 | | | | | | | | | 9 |
| | | | | | | | | | |
| | | | | | | | | | 100 |

Look at the shaded square.

2 | | | | | | | | | 9 |
| | | | | | | | | | |
| | | | | | | | | | 99 | 100 |

Use patterns to write the number.

> 99 is before 100.
> 99 is below 9.

1				5					10
				25					
							38		
	52					57			
									80
81									
					96				

Home Note: Your child uses addition patterns to write numbers on a hundred chart.

Add 10 Problems

1

I collected _____ pebbles.
Then I collected _____ more.
How many did I collect?
(31, 10)

Read the problem using
the pair of numbers.

2

$31 = \underline{3}$ tens $+ \underline{1}$ one
$31 + 10 = \underline{4}$ tens $+ \underline{1}$ one
$31 + 10 = \underline{41}$

Complete the equations.

3

I collected $\underline{41}$ pebbles.

Write the solution.

I collected _____ pebbles.
Then I collected _____ more.
How many pebbles did I collect?
(43, 10)   (79, 10)   (52, 10)

---

① (43, 10)

$43 = \underline{}$ tens $+ \underline{}$ ones
$43 + 10 = \underline{}$ tens $+ \underline{}$ ones
$43 + 10 = \underline{}$

I collected _____ pebbles.

② (79, 10)

$79 = \underline{}$ tens $+ \underline{}$ ones
$79 + 10 = \underline{}$ tens $+ \underline{}$ ones
$79 + 10 = \underline{}$

I collected _____ pebbles.

③ (52, 10)

$52 = \underline{}$ tens $+ \underline{}$ ones
$52 + 10 = \underline{}$ tens $+ \underline{}$ ones
$52 + 10 = \underline{}$

I collected _____ pebbles.

Home Note: Your child solves word problems by adding 10 to two-digit numbers.

Game Rules for Pathways to 100

HOW TO PLAY

What you need

- number cube (1 & 10)
- *WorkSpace* page 27
- pencil

➤ **Start at 1.**

➤ **Players take turns. Each turn has four steps.**

1

Roll the cube.

2

1		
11		

Add 1 or 10.
Write the sum in the correct square.

3

    $1 + 10 = 11$

Write the equation.

4

Pass the cube to your partner.

➤ **The winner is the first player who lands on 100.**

Home Note: Your child practices adding 1 and 10 to numbers by playing a game.

Pathways to 100

DIRECTIONS

➤ Use the rules on page 26.

1				5	6	7			
11	12	13	14			17	18	19	
								29	
								39	
								49	
								59	
								69	
								79	
								89	
								99	100

Equations

10 + 3 = 13	7 + 5 = 12	10 + 29 = 39
1 + 4 = 5	2 + 12 = 14	10 + 39 = 49
1 + 6 = 7	3 + 14 = 17	10 + 49 = 59
1 + 5 = 6	1 + 17 = 18	10 + 59 = 69
10 + 6 = 16	1 + 18 = 19	10 × 69 = 89
7 + 4 = 11	10 + 19 = 29	10 + 89 = 99

Home Note: Your child practices adding 1 and 10 to numbers by playing a game.

Add Multiples of 10 on a 1 to 100 Chart

DIRECTIONS

1

I read ___54___ pages of my book.
Then I read ___40___ more.
How many pages did I read in all?
(54, 40)

Read the problem using
the pair of numbers.

2

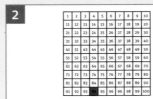

Color the sum on
the 1 to 100 chart.

3

$54 + 40 = 94$

Write the equation.

I read _____ pages of my book.
Then I read _____ more.
How many pages did I read in all?

(73, 10)   (49, 30)   (61, 20)

1	2	3	4	5	6	7	8	9	10
11	12	13	14	15	16	17	18	19	20
21	22	23	24	25	26	27	28	29	30
31	32	33	34	35	36	37	38	39	40
41	42	43	44	45	46	47	48	49	50
51	52	53	54	55	56	57	58	59	60
61	62	63	64	65	66	67	68	69	70
71	72	73	74	75	76	77	78	79	80
81	82	83	84	85	86	87	88	89	90
91	92	93	94	95	96	97	98	99	100

① (73, 10)   73 × 10 = 83

② (49, 30)   49 + 30 = 79

③ (61, 20)   61 + 20 = 81

Home Note: Your child adds multiples of 10 to numbers on a 1 to 100 chart.

Go to the Next 10

1

_____ children were at the playground.
_____ more children came.
How many children are there in all?
(19, 3)

Read the problem.

2

1	2	3	4	5	6	7	8	9	10
11	12	13	14	15	16	17	18	19	20
21	22	23	24	25	26	27	28	29	30
31	32	33	34	35	36	37	38	39	40

Show the problem on
the 1 to 100 chart.

3

$$19 + 3$$
$$\underline{19} + \underline{1} = \underline{20}$$
$$\underline{20} + \underline{2} = \underline{22}$$
$$19 + 3 = \underline{22}$$

Write equations
to go to the next 10
and to add the spillover.
Write the sum.

_____ children were at the playground.
_____ more children came.
How many children are there in all?
(47, 6)   (24, 7)

---

① (47, 6)

$$47 + 6$$

$$\underline{47} + \underline{3} = \underline{50}$$
$$\underline{47} + \underline{3} = \underline{53}$$
$$47 + 6 = \underline{53}$$

1	2	3	4	5	6	7	8	9	10
11	12	13	14	15	16	17	18	19	20
21	22	23	24	25	26	27	28	29	30
31	32	33	34	35	36	37	38	39	40
41	42	43	44	45	46	47	48	49	50
51	52	53	54	55	65	57	58	59	60
61	62	63	64	65	66	67	68	69	70
71	72	73	74	75	76	77	78	79	80
81	82	83	84	85	86	78	88	89	90

---

② (24, 7)

$$24 + 7$$

$$\underline{24} + \underline{6} = \underline{30}$$
$$\underline{30} + \underline{1} = \underline{31}$$
$$24 + 7 = \underline{31}$$

1	2	3	4	5	6	7	8	9	10
11	12	13	14	15	16	17	18	19	20
21	22	23	24	25	26	27	28	29	30
31	32	33	34	35	36	37	38	39	40
41	42	43	44	45	46	47	48	49	50
51	52	53	54	55	65	57	58	59	60
61	62	63	64	65	66	67	68	69	70
71	72	73	74	75	76	77	78	79	80
81	82	83	84	85	86	78	88	89	90

Home Note: Your child demonstrates that he or she can add one digit
to two digits by using a 1 to 100 chart to help solve equations.

Go to the Next 10

1

_____ children were at the playground.
_____ more children came.
How many children are there in all?
(19, 3)

Read the problem.

2

1	2	3	4	5	6	7	8	9	10
11	12	13	14	15	16	17	18	19	20
21	22	23	24	25	26	27	28	29	30
31	32	33	34	35	36	37	38	39	40

Show the problem on
the 1 to 100 chart.

3

$$19 + 3$$
$$\underline{19 + 1} = 20$$
$$\underline{20 + 2} = 22$$
$$19 + 3 = \underline{22}$$

Write equations
to go to the next 10
and to add the spillover.
Write the sum.

_____ children were at the playground.
_____ more children came.
How many children are there in all?
(34, 8)   (52, 9)

---

① **(34, 8)**

$$34 + 8$$

$$\underline{34} + \underline{4} = \underline{40}$$

$$\underline{34} + \underline{8} = \underline{40}$$

$$34 + 8 = \underline{42}$$

1	2	3	4	5	6	7	8	9	10
11	12	13	14	15	16	17	18	19	20
21	22	23	24	25	26	27	28	29	30
31	32	33	34	35	36	37	38	39	40
41	42	43	44	45	46	47	48	49	50
51	52	53	54	55	65	57	58	59	60
61	62	63	64	65	66	67	68	69	70
71	72	73	74	75	76	77	78	79	80
81	82	83	84	85	86	78	88	89	90

② **(52, 9)**

$$52 + 9$$

$$\underline{52} + \underline{8} = \underline{60}$$

$$\underline{52} + \underline{9} = \underline{61}$$

$$52 + 9 = \underline{61}$$

1	2	3	4	5	6	7	8	9	10
11	12	13	14	15	16	17	18	19	20
21	22	23	24	25	26	27	28	29	30
31	32	33	34	35	36	37	38	39	40
41	42	43	44	45	46	47	48	49	50
51	52	53	54	55	65	57	58	59	60
61	62	63	64	65	66	67	68	69	70
71	72	73	74	75	76	77	78	79	80
81	82	83	84	85	86	78	88	89	90

Home Note: Your child demonstrates that he or she can add one digit
to two digits by using a 1 to 100 chart to help solve equations.

Game Rules for 101 and Out

HOW TO PLAY

What you need
- number cube (1–6)
- *WorkSpace* page 32 or 33
- pencil

➤ **Players take turns, for up to 6 rolls each.**

1

Player A		Player B	
Roll 1 5	1 + ___ = ___	Roll 1	1 + ___ = ___
Roll 2	___ + ___ = ___	Roll 2	___ + ___ = ___

Roll the cube and record it.

2

Player A		Player B	
Roll 1 5	1 + _5_ = _6_	Roll 1	1 + ___ = ___
Roll 2	___ + ___ = ___	Roll 2	___ + ___ = ___

Decide whether to use the roll as tens or ones.
Add to your starting number.

3

Player A		Player B	
Roll 1 5	1 + _5_ = _6_	Roll 1	1 + ___ = ___
Roll 2	_6_ + ___ = ___	Roll 2	___ + ___ = ___

Record the sum as your starting number for the next turn.

4

 ➡

Pass the cube to your partner.

➤ **The winner is the player whose total score is closer to 100.**
A player who goes over 100 is out!

Home Note: Your child practices adding ones and tens to numbers by playing a game.

101 and Out

HOW TO PLAY

1

Player A	
Roll 1 __5__	1 + ___ = ___
Roll 2 ___	___ + ___ = ___

Roll the cube and record it.

2

Player A	
Roll 1 __5__	1 + __50__ = __51__
Roll 2 ___	___ + ___ = ___

Decide whether to use
the roll as tens or ones.
Add to your starting number.

3

Player A	
Roll 1 __5__	1 + __50__ = __51__
Roll 2 ___	__51__ + ___ = ___

Record the sum as
your starting number
for the next turn.
Pass the cube to your partner.

Player A		Player B	
Roll 1 ____	1 + 40 = 41	Roll 1 ____	1 + 40 = 41
Roll 2 ____	80 + 60 = 140	Roll 2 ____	60 + 50 = 110
Roll 3 ____	70 + 60 = 130	Roll 3 ____	70 + 60 = 130
Roll 4 ____	100 + 70 = 70	Roll 4 ____	60 + 50 = 110
Roll 5 ____	60 + 40 = 100	Roll 5 ____	60 + 60 = 120
Roll 6 ____	90 + 40 = 130	Roll 6 ____	70 + 50 = 100
Final Score		**Final Score**	

Home Note: Your child practices adding ones and tens to numbers by playing a game.

101 and Out

1

Player A	
Roll 1 _5_	1 + ___ = ___
Roll 2 ___	___ + ___ = ___

Roll the cube and record it.

2

Player A	
Roll 1 _5_	1 + _50_ = _51_
Roll 2 ___	___ + ___ = ___

Decide whether to use
the roll as tens or ones.
Add to your starting number.

3

Player A	
Roll 1 _5_	1 + _50_ = _51_
Roll 2 ___	_51_ + ___ = ___

Record the sum as
your starting number
for the next turn.
Pass the cube to your partner.

Player A		Player B	
Roll 1 ____	1 + _20_ = _21_	Roll 1 ____	1 + _70_ = _71_
Roll 2 ____	_90_ + _40_ = _130_	Roll 2 ____	_90_ + _60_ = _150_
Roll 3 ____	_60_ + _40_ = _100_	Roll 3 ____	_70_ + _40_ = _110_
Roll 4 ____	_30_ + _40_ = _70_	Roll 4 ____	_80_ + _10_ = _90_
Roll 5 ____	_20_ + _50_ = _80_	Roll 5 ____	_80_ + _20_ = _100_
Roll 6 ____	_90_ + _10_ = _100_	Roll 6 ____	_50_ + _10_ = _60_
Final Score		**Final Score**	

Home Note: Your child practices adding ones and tens to numbers by playing a game.

Show What You Know

DIRECTIONS

➤ Use the 1 to 100 chart on page 35 to help you find each sum.

➤ Write equations for problems 5 and 6.

① 43 + 10 = 53

② 30 + 40 = 70

③ 67 + 20 = 87

④ 58 + 9 = 78

⑤ Sam has 22 toy cars.
His mother gives him 10 more.
How many toy cars does Sam have now?

22 + 10 = 32

⑥ Katie blew up 16 balloons.
Then she blew up 5 more.
How many balloons did Katie blow up in all?

16 + 5 = 21

Home Note: Your child uses a 1 to 100 chart to add multiples of 10 and one-digit numbers to numbers.

1 to 100 Chart

1	2	3	4	5	6	7	8	9	10
11	12	13	14	15	16	17	18	19	20
21	22	23	24	25	26	27	28	29	30
31	32	33	34	35	36	37	38	39	40
41	42	43	44	45	46	47	48	49	50
51	52	53	54	55	56	57	58	59	60
61	62	63	64	65	66	67	68	69	70
71	72	73	74	75	76	77	78	79	80
81	82	83	84	85	86	87	88	89	90
91	92	93	94	95	96	97	98	99	100

Home Note: Your child uses a 1 to 100 chart to add multiples of 10 and one-digit numbers to numbers.

Solve Problems

DIRECTIONS

1

60, 10

Use each number pair to solve the problem.

2

57	58	59	60
67	68	69	70
77	78	79	80

Show the answer on the 1 to 100 chart.

3

$$60 \xrightarrow{+10} 70$$

Show the answer with an open number line.

4

$$60 + 10 = 70$$

Write the equation for the problem.

I picked _40_ flowers.

Then I picked _10_ more.

How many flowers did I pick in all?

(30, 10)   (34, 20)   (57, 20)

---

① 30, 10

1 to 100 Chart

1	2	3	4	5	6	7	8	9	10
11	12	13	14	15	16	17	18	19	20
21	22	23	24	25	26	27	28	29	30
31	32	33	34	35	36	37	38	39	40
41	42	43	44	45	46	47	48	49	50
51	52	53	54	55	56	57	58	59	60
61	62	63	64	65	66	67	68	69	70
71	72	73	74	75	76	77	78	79	80
81	82	83	84	85	86	87	88	89	90
91	92	93	94	95	96	97	98	99	100

Open Number Line

Equation

30 + 10 = 40

Home Note: Your child uses a 1 to 100 chart and open number lines to add 10 and 20 to two-digit numbers.

② 34, 20

1 to 100 Chart

1	2	3	4	5	6	7	8	9	10
11	12	13	14	15	16	17	18	19	20
21	22	23	24	25	26	27	28	29	30
31	32	33	34	35	36	37	38	39	40
41	42	43	44	45	46	47	48	49	50
51	52	53	54	55	56	57	58	59	60
61	62	63	64	65	66	67	68	69	70
71	72	73	74	75	76	77	78	79	80
81	82	83	84	85	86	87	88	89	90
91	92	93	94	95	96	97	98	99	100

Open Number Line

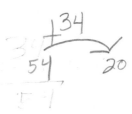

Equation

34+20 54

③ 57, 20

1 to 100 Chart

1	2	3	4	5	6	7	8	9	10
11	12	13	14	15	16	17	18	19	20
21	22	23	24	25	26	27	28	29	30
31	32	33	34	35	36	37	38	39	40
41	42	43	44	45	46	47	48	49	50
51	52	53	54	55	56	57	58	59	60
61	62	63	64	65	66	67	68	69	70
71	72	73	74	75	76	77	78	79	80
81	82	83	84	85	86	87	88	89	90
91	92	93	94	95	96	97	98	99	100

Open Number Line

Equation

57 , 20 : 77

Home Note: Your child uses a 1 to 100 chart and an open number line to add 10 and 20 to two-digit numbers.

Lesson 21

37

Solve Problems

1

60, 10

Use each number pair to solve the problem.

2

57	58	59	60
67	68	69	70
77	78	79	80

Show the answer on the 1 to 100 chart.

3

$$60 \overset{+10}{\curvearrowright} 70$$

Show the answer with an open number line.

4

$$60 + 10 = 70$$

Write the equation for the problem.

I picked _20_ flowers.

Then I picked _70_ more.

How many flowers did I pick in all?

(20, 70)   (50, 40)   (47, 50)

---

1 20, 70

1 to 100 Chart

1	2	3	4	5	6	7	8	9	10
11	12	13	14	15	16	17	18	19	20
21	22	23	24	25	26	27	28	29	30
31	32	33	34	35	36	37	38	39	40
41	42	43	44	45	46	47	48	49	50
51	52	53	54	55	56	57	58	59	60
61	62	63	64	65	66	67	68	69	70
71	72	73	74	75	76	77	78	79	80
81	82	83	84	85	86	87	88	89	90
91	92	93	94	95	96	97	98	99	100

Open Number Line

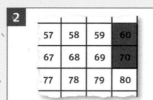

$$20 \overset{+10}{\curvearrowright} 90$$

Equation

70 + 20 90

Home Note: Your child uses a 1 to 100 chart and open number lines to add multiples of 10 to two-digit numbers.

② 50, 40

1 to 100 Chart

1	2	3	4	5	6	7	8	9	10
11	12	13	14	15	16	17	18	19	20
21	22	23	24	25	26	27	28	29	30
31	32	33	34	35	36	37	38	39	40
41	42	43	44	45	46	47	48	49	50
51	52	53	54	55	56	57	58	59	60
61	62	63	64	65	66	67	68	69	70
71	72	73	74	75	76	77	78	79	80
81	82	83	84	85	86	87	88	89	90
91	92	93	94	95	96	97	98	99	100

Open Number Line

50 +40 80

Equation

50 + 40 = 80

③ 47, 50

1 to 100 Chart

1	2	3	4	5	6	7	8	9	10
11	12	13	14	15	16	17	18	19	20
21	22	23	24	25	26	27	28	29	30
31	32	33	34	35	36	37	38	39	40
41	42	43	44	45	46	47	48	49	50
51	52	53	54	55	56	57	58	59	60
61	62	63	64	65	66	67	68	69	70
71	72	73	74	75	76	77	78	79	80
81	82	83	84	85	86	87	88	89	90
91	92	93	94	95	96	97	98	99	100

Open Number Line

50 + 47 = 87

Equation

50 + 47 = 87

50
+ 47
87

Home Note: Your child uses a 1 to 100 chart and open number lines to add multiples of 10 to two-digit numbers.

Add by Going to the Next Ten

DIRECTIONS

1

37, 8

Use each number pair for the problem.

2

21	22	23	24	25	26	27	28	29	30
31	32	33	34	35	36	37	38	39	40
41	51	43	44	45	46	47	48	49	50
51	52	53	54	55	56	57	58	59	60
61	62	63	64	65	66	67	68	69	70
71	72	73	74	75	76	77	78	79	80
81	82	83	84	85	86	87	88	89	90
91	92	93	94	95	96	96	98	99	100

Show the problem on the 1 to 100 chart.

3

$$37 \overset{+3}{\longrightarrow} 40 \overset{+5}{\longrightarrow} 45$$

Show the addition with an open number line.

4

$$37 + 8 = 45$$

Write the addition equation.

I saved $_____.

Then I saved $_____ more.

How much did I save in all?

(48, 5)   (29, 7)   (16, 6)

---

① 48, 5

1 to 100 Chart

1	2	3	4	5	6	7	8	9	10
11	12	13	14	15	16	17	18	19	20
21	22	23	24	25	26	27	28	29	30
31	32	33	34	35	36	37	38	39	40
41	42	43	44	45	46	47	48	49	50
51	52	53	54	55	56	57	58	59	60
61	62	63	64	65	66	67	68	69	70
71	72	73	74	75	76	77	78	79	80
81	82	83	84	85	86	87	88	89	90
91	92	93	94	95	96	97	98	99	100

Open Number Line

48 ⟶ 53

Equation

48 + 5 = 53

Home Note: Your child adds one-digit numbers to two-digit numbers by going to the next ten.

② 29, 7

1 to 100 Chart

1	2	3	4	5	6	7	8	9	10
11	12	13	14	15	16	17	18	19	20
21	22	23	24	25	26	27	28	29	30
31	32	33	34	35	36	37	38	39	40
41	42	43	44	45	46	47	48	49	50
51	52	53	54	55	56	57	58	59	60
61	62	63	64	65	66	67	68	69	70
71	72	73	74	75	76	77	78	79	80
81	82	83	84	85	86	87	88	89	90
91	92	93	94	95	96	97	98	99	100

Open Number Line

$$29 \xrightarrow{+7} 36$$

Equation

$$29 + 7 = 36$$

③ 16, 6

1 to 100 Chart

1	2	3	4	5	6	7	8	9	10
11	12	13	14	15	16	17	18	19	20
21	22	23	24	25	26	27	28	29	30
31	32	33	34	35	36	37	38	39	40
41	42	43	44	45	46	47	48	49	50
51	52	53	54	55	56	57	58	59	60
61	62	63	64	65	66	67	68	69	70
71	72	73	74	75	76	77	78	79	80
81	82	83	84	85	86	87	88	89	90
91	92	93	94	95	96	97	98	99	100

Open Number Line

$$16 \xrightarrow{+6} 22$$

Equation

$$16 + 6 = 22$$

Home Note: Your child adds one-digit numbers to two-digit numbers by going to the next ten.

Add Tens and Then Ones

1

21	22	23	24	25	26	27	28	29	30
31	32	33	34	35	36	37	38	39	40
41	51	43	44	45	46	47	48	49	50
51	52	53	54	55	56	57	58	59	60
61	62	63	64	65	66	67	68	69	70
71	72	73	74	75	76	77	78	79	80

38 + 29

Color the 1 to 100 chart to show the addition.

2

$$38 \xrightarrow{+20} 58 \xrightarrow{+2} 60 \xrightarrow{+7} 67$$

Show the addition with an open number line.

3

38 + 29 = __67__

Write the sum.

1	2	3	4	5	6	7	8	9	10
11	12	13	14	15	16	17	18	19	20
21	22	23	24	25	26	27	28	29	30
31	32	33	34	35	36	37	38	39	40
41	42	43	44	45	46	47	48	49	50
51	52	53	54	55	56	57	58	59	60
61	62	63	64	65	66	67	68	69	70
71	72	73	74	75	76	77	78	79	80
81	82	83	84	85	86	87	88	89	90
91	92	93	94	95	96	97	98	99	100

26 + 57 = 67

26
57
___
67

Home Note: Your child uses a 1 to 100 chart and an open number line to add two two-digit numbers.

Add Tens and Then Ones

DIRECTIONS

1

21	22	23	24	25	26	27	28	29	30
31	32	33	34	35	36	37	38	39	40
41	51	43	44	45	46	47	48	49	50
51	52	53	54	55	56	57	58	59	60
61	62	63	64	65	66	67	68	69	70
71	72	73	74	75	76	77	78	79	80

38 + 29

Color the 1 to 100 chart to show the addition.

2

$$38 \xrightarrow{+20} 58 \xrightarrow{+2} 60 \xrightarrow{+7} 67$$

Show the addition with an open number line.

3

38 + 29 = 67

Write the equation.

I saved $ __36__ .

Then I saved $ __17__ more.

How much did I save in all?

(36, 17)   (48, 25)   (55, 26)

---

① 36, 17

1 to 100 Chart

1	2	3	4	5	6	7	8	9	10
11	12	13	14	15	16	17	18	19	20
21	22	23	24	25	26	27	28	29	30
31	32	33	34	35	36	37	38	39	40
41	42	43	44	45	46	47	48	49	50
51	52	53	54	55	56	57	58	59	60
61	62	63	64	65	66	67	68	69	70
71	72	73	74	75	76	77	78	79	80
81	82	83	84	85	86	87	88	89	90
91	92	93	94	95	96	97	98	99	100

Open Number Line

Equation

36 + 17 = 53

Home Note: Your child adds two-digit numbers to two-digit numbers by going to the next 10.

② 48, 25

1 to 100 Chart

1	2	3	4	5	6	7	8	9	10
11	12	13	14	15	16	17	18	19	20
21	22	23	24	25	26	27	28	29	30
31	32	33	34	35	36	37	38	39	40
41	42	43	44	45	46	47	(48)	49	50
51	52	53	54	55	56	57	58	59	60
61	62	63	64	65	66	67	68	69	70
71	72	73	74	75	76	77	78	79	80
81	82	83	84	85	86	87	88	89	90
91	92	93	94	95	96	97	98	99	100

Open Number Line

$$48 + 25$$
$$73$$

Equation

$$48 + 25 = 15$$

③ 55, 26

1 to 100 Chart

1	2	3	4	5	6	7	8	9	10
11	12	13	14	15	16	17	18	19	20
21	22	23	24	25	26	27	28	29	30
31	32	33	34	35	36	37	38	39	40
41	42	43	44	45	46	47	48	49	50
51	52	53	54	55	56	57	58	59	60
61	62	63	64	65	66	67	68	69	70
71	72	73	74	75	76	77	78	79	80
81	82	83	84	85	86	87	88	89	90
91	92	93	94	95	96	97	98	99	100

Open Number Line

$$55 + 26$$

Equation

Home Note: Your child adds two-digit numbers to two-digit numbers by going to the next 10.

Game Rules for 101 and Out—with an Open Number Line

What you need

- number cube (1–6)
- *WorkSpace* page 46 or 47
- pencil

➤ **Players take turns for up to 6 rolls each.**

1

Roll	Open Number Line	Equation
Roll 1 _4_	1	1 + __ = __

Roll the cube and record it.

2

Roll	Open Number Line	Equation
Roll 1 _4_	1 $\xrightarrow{+40}$ 41	1 + ___ = ___

Decide whether to use the roll as tens or ones.
Add with an open number line.

3

Roll	Open Number Line	Equation
Roll 1 _4_	1 $\xrightarrow{+40}$ 41	1 + _40_ = _41_
Roll 2 __	41	41

Write an addition equation.
Write the sum as your next starting number.

4

Pass the cube to your partner.

➤ **The winner is the player whose total score is closer to 100.**
A player who goes over 100 is out!

Home Note: Your child practices adding one-digit numbers
and multiples of 10 to numbers by playing a game.

101 and Out—
with an Open Number Line

HOW TO PLAY

➤ Players take turns for up to 6 rolls each.

1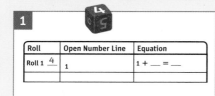

Roll	Open Number Line	Equation
Roll 1 _4_	1	1 + ___ = ___

Roll the cube and record it.

2

Roll	Open Number Line
Roll 1 _4_	1 +40 ↗ 41

Decide whether to use the roll as tens or ones. Add with an open number line.

3

Open Number Line	Equation
1 +40 ↗ 41	1 + _40_ = _41_
41	41

Write an addition equation. Write the sum as your next starting number.

4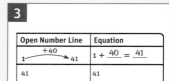

Pass the cube to your partner.

➤ The winner is the player whose total score is closer to 100.

➤ A player who goes over 100 is out!

Roll	Open Number Line	Equation
Roll 1 ____	1	1 + ____ = ____
Roll 2 ____		
Roll 3 ____		
Roll 4 ____		
Roll 5 ____		
Roll 6 ____		
Final Score		

Lesson 25

Home Note: Your child practices adding one-digit numbers and multiples of 10 to numbers by playing a game.

101 and Out—
with an Open Number Line

HOW TO PLAY

➤ **Players take turns for up to 6 rolls each.**

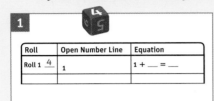

Roll the cube and record it.

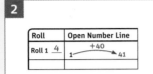

Decide whether to use the roll as tens or ones. Add with an open number line.

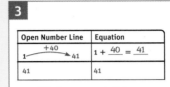

Write an addition equation. Write the sum as your next starting number.

Pass the cube to your partner.

➤ **The winner is the player whose total score is closer to 100.**

➤ **A player who goes over 100 is out!**

Roll	Open Number Line	Equation
Roll 1 ____	1	1 + _____
Roll 2 ____		_____
Roll 3 ____		_____
Roll 4 ____		_____
Roll 5 ____		_____
Roll 6 ____		_____
Final Score		

Home Note: Your child practices adding one-digit numbers and multiples of 10 to numbers by playing a game.

Show What You Know

1

25, 16

Use the number pair for the problem.

2

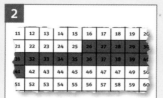

Show the problem on the hundred chart.

3

+10 +5 +1
25   35   40 41

Show the addition with an open number line.

4

25 + 16 = 41

Write an addition equation.

I counted _____ ants marching across the floor.

Then I counted _____ more.

How many ants did I count?

(23, 40)   (34, 8)   (68, 17)

---

① 23, 40

1 to 100 Chart

1	2	3	4	5	6	7	8	9	10
11	12	13	14	15	16	17	18	19	20
21	22	23	24	25	26	27	28	29	30
31	32	33	34	35	36	37	38	39	40
41	42	43	44	45	46	47	48	49	50
51	52	53	54	55	56	57	58	59	60
61	62	63	64	65	66	67	68	69	70
71	72	73	74	75	76	77	78	79	80
81	82	83	84	85	86	87	88	89	90
91	92	93	94	95	96	97	98	99	100

Open Number Line

Equation

_____

Home Note: Your child uses a hundred chart and open number lines to add numbers to two-digit numbers.

② 34, 8

1 to 100 Chart

1	2	3	4	5	6	7	8	9	10
11	12	13	14	15	16	17	18	19	20
21	22	23	24	25	26	27	28	29	30
31	32	33	34	35	36	37	38	39	40
41	42	43	44	45	46	47	48	49	50
51	52	53	54	55	56	57	58	59	60
61	62	63	64	65	66	67	68	69	70
71	72	73	74	75	76	77	78	79	80
81	82	83	84	85	86	87	88	89	90
91	92	93	94	95	96	97	98	99	100

Open Number Line

Equation

_____

③ 68, 17

1 to 100 Chart

1	2	3	4	5	6	7	8	9	10
11	12	13	14	15	16	17	18	19	20
21	22	23	24	25	26	27	28	29	30
31	32	33	34	35	36	37	38	39	40
41	42	43	44	45	46	47	48	49	50
51	52	53	54	55	56	57	58	59	60
61	62	63	64	65	66	67	68	69	70
71	72	73	74	75	76	77	78	79	80
81	82	83	84	85	86	87	88	89	90
91	92	93	94	95	96	97	98	99	100

Open Number Line

Equation

_____

Home Note: Your child uses a hundred chart and open number lines to add numbers to two-digit numbers.

Lesson 25

49

Use Splitting to Add

1

Tom counted 54 penguins and 12 wolves. How many animals did he count in all?

Read the problem.

2

$54 + 12$

$50 + 10 = 60$

$4 + 2 = 6$

$60 + 6 = 66$

$54 + 12 = 66$

Split the numbers to add.

3

$$\begin{array}{r} 54 \\ +12 \\ \hline 60 \\ +\ 6 \\ \hline 66 \end{array}$$

Add going down.

4

$$54 \xrightarrow{+10} 64 \xrightarrow{+2} 66$$

Add with an open number line.

---

(1) **Tom counted 23 pythons and 36 goats. How many animals did he count in all?**

Split the numbers to add.

Add going down.

Add with an open number line.

Home Note: Your child uses the splitting strategy to solve word problems.

(2) Tom counted 61 bears and 23 pythons. How many animals did he count in all?

Split the numbers to add.	Add going down.

Add with an open number line.

(3) Tom counted 54 penguins and 45 pirates. How many things did he count in all?

Split the numbers to add.	Add going down.

Add with an open number line.

Home Note: Your child uses the splitting strategy to solve word problems.

Lesson 26

51

Buy Stuffed Animals

DIRECTIONS

1

Penguin $13
and
Sheep $18

13 + 18

Choose two
stuffed animals.
Write the problem.

2

$$10 + 10 = 20$$
$$3 + 8 = 11$$
$$20 + 11 = 31$$
$$13 + 18 = 31$$

Find the total price
using equations.

3

13
+18
20
+ 11
31

Find the total
price going down.

4

+10 +7 +1
13   23 30 31

Add with an
open number line.

STUFFED ANIMALS

Penguin $13	Bear $35
Sheep $18	Wolf $38
Ghost $26	Pirate $39
Python $29	Tiger $47
Goat $34	Rabbit $49

① Stuffed animals: _____ and _____

Problem _____

Use equations.

Add going down.

Use an open number line.

Home Note: Your child uses splitting and going to the next ten to add two-digit numbers.

② Stuffed animals: _____ and _____

Problem _____

Use equations.	Add going down.

Use an open number line.

③ Stuffed animals: _____ and _____

Problem _____

Use equations.	Add going down.

Use an open number line.

Home Note: Your child uses splitting and going to the next ten to add two-digit numbers.

Buy Stuffed Animals

DIRECTIONS

1

Penguin $13
and
Sheep $18

13 + 18

Choose two stuffed animals. Write the problem.

2

10 + 10 = 20
3 + 8 = 11
20 + 11 = 31
13 + 18 = 31

Find the total price using equations.

3

13
+18
20
+ 11
31

Find the total price going down.

4

+10 +7 +1
13 → 23 → 30 → 31

Add with an open number line.

STUFFED ANIMALS

Penguin $13	Bear $35
Sheep $18	Wolf. $38
Ghost $26	Pirate $39
Python $29	Tiger $47
Goat $34	Rabbit. $49

① Stuffed animals: _____ and _____

Problem _____

Use equations.

Add going down.

Use an open number line.

Home Note: Your child uses splitting and going to the next ten to add two-digit numbers.

(2) **Stuffed animals:** _____ and _____

Problem _____

Use equations.	**Add going down.**

Use an open number line.

(3) **Stuffed animals:** _____ and _____

Problem _____

Use equations.	**Add going down.**

Use an open number line.

Home Note: Your child uses splitting and going to the next ten to add two-digit numbers.

Write About Addition

➤ Tell about addition with words, numbers, and pictures.

ABOUT ADDITION

Home Note: Your child writes about addition.

Show What You Know

DIRECTIONS

1

21	22	23	24	25	26	27	28	29	30
31	32	33	34	35	36	37	38	39	40
41	51	43	44	45	46	47	48	49	50
51	52	53	54	55	56	57	58	59	60
61	62	63	64	65	66	67	68	69	70
71	72	73	74	75	76	77	78	79	80

$38 + 29$

Color the 1 to 100 chart
to show the addition.

2

$$\overset{+20}{38} \nearrow \overset{+2}{58} \nearrow \overset{+7}{60} \nearrow 67$$

Show the addition with
an open number line.

3

$38 + 29 = 67$

Write the
addition equation.

I saved $_____.

Then I saved $_____ more.

How much did I save in all?

① 34, 48

1 to 100 Chart

1	2	3	4	5	6	7	8	9	10
11	12	13	14	15	16	17	18	19	20
21	22	23	24	25	26	27	28	29	30
31	32	33	34	35	36	37	38	39	40
41	42	43	44	45	46	47	48	49	50
51	52	53	54	55	56	57	58	59	60
61	62	63	64	65	66	67	68	69	70
71	72	73	74	75	76	77	78	79	80
81	82	83	84	85	86	87	88	89	90
91	92	93	94	95	96	97	98	99	100

Open Number Line

Equation

_____

Home Note: Your child adds two-digit numbers using a 1 to 100 chart and an open number line.

Show What You Know

➤ Use the prices on the chart to solve each problem.

The stuffed animals have gone on sale. Here are the new prices.

STUFFED ANIMALS

Penguin	$6	Bear	$21
Sheep	$9	Wolf	$24
Ghost	$10	Pirate	$27
Python	$15	Tiger	$29
Goat	$18	Rabbit	$38

(1) Stuffed animals: Ghost $ _____ and Goat $_____
Problem _____

Use equations.	Add going down.

Use an open number line.

(2) Stuffed animals: Python $ _____ and Wolf $_____
Problem _____

Use equations.	Add going down.

Use an open number line.

Home Note: Your child uses various strategies to solve word problems involving addition of two-digit numbers.

(3) Stuffed animals: Bear $ _____ and Rabbit $_____

Problem _____

Use equations.	Add going down.
Use an open number line.	

(4) Stuffed animals: Tiger $ _____ and Pirate $_____

Problem _____

Use equations.	Add going down.
Use an open number line.	

(5) Choose two stuffed animals to buy. How much would you spend?

Stuffed animals: _____ and_____

Problem _____

Use equations.	Add going down.
Use an open number line.	

 Home Note: Your child uses various strategies to solve word problems involving addition of two-digit numbers.

101 and Out— with an Open Number Line

> Players take turns for up to 6 rolls each.

1

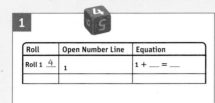

Roll	Open Number Line	Equation
Roll 1 __4__	1	1 + ___ = ___

Roll the cube and record it.

2

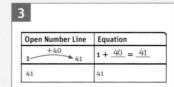

Roll	Open Number Line
Roll 1 __4__	1 ⌒+40⌒ 41

Decide whether to use the roll as tens or ones. Add with an open number line.

3

Open Number Line	Equation
1 ⌒+40⌒ 41	1 + __40__ = __41__
41	41

Write an addition equation. Write the sum as your next starting number.

4

Pass the cube to your partner.

> The winner is the player whose total score is closer to 100.

> A player who goes over 100 is out!

Roll	Open Number Line	Equation
Roll 1 _____	1	1 + ___ = ___
Roll 2 _____		
Roll 3 _____		
Roll 4 _____		
Roll 5 _____		
Roll 6 _____		
Final Score		

Home Note: Your child practices adding one-digit numbers and multiples of 10 to numbers by playing a game.

Math Vocabulary

DIRECTIONS

➤ Write new words and terms in the box.

➤ Write a definition, show an example, or draw a picture for each word or term in your list.

Home Note: Your child creates a math vocabulary list.

Math Vocabulary

➤ Write new words and terms in the box.

➤ Write a definition, show an example, or draw a picture for each word or term in your list.

Home Note: Your child creates a math vocabulary list.

Glossary

add

To *add* means to combine two numbers to find out how many in all. For example, we can *add* or combine 4 and 2 and we can write it like this: $4 + 2$. The plus symbol $+$ tells you to add.

$4 + 2$ asks the question, *How many in all?* If there are 4 tiles and 2 tiles, the total is 6 tiles. One way to add is to count them all. Another would be to begin at 4 and count two more.

This ten frame shows $4 + 2 = 6$.

addend

In the equation $4 + 2 = 6$, the two numbers being added are called *addends*. 4 and 2 are *addends*; 6 is the sum. There may be many *addends*. In $1 + 2 + 3 + 4 = 10$, 1, 2, 3, and 4 are all *addends*.

addition

Addition is the name for what you do when you add. When you add two numbers together you are doing *addition*.

addition equation

An *addition equation* is a number sentence with an equal sign to show that two amounts have the same value. There is addition on one or both sides of the equal sign. For example, $12 = 3 + 3 + 3 + 3$ is an *addition equation*.

equal

Equal means the same amount. For example, twelve is equal to five plus seven. The symbol for *equal* is $=$.

equation

An *equation* is a number sentence that uses an equal sign to show that two amounts have the same value.

For example, $3 + 4 = 7$. Both sides have the same value, 7.

multiples of ten

When you start with 10 and count by tens, the numbers you get are called *multiples of ten*.

10, 20, 30, 40, 50, . . . are *multiples of ten*.

We say 20 is a *multiple of ten* because it is a number you get when counting by tens.

open number line

An *open number line* is a way to record the distance or difference between two numbers. For example, to solve the problem $27 + \underline{} = 37$ you can show the distance from 27 to 37 by drawing a curved arrow between them and write +10 above the curve.

$$27 + \underline{} = 37 \qquad \overset{+10}{\overset{\frown}{27 \qquad 37}}$$

Glossary

plus

The word *plus* tells you to add. 3 *plus* 3 means you should add 3 and 3. The symbol for plus is $+$.

sum

The *sum* is the answer you get when you add two or more numbers. In the addition equation $2 + 3 + 5 = 10$, 10 is the *sum*.

We can ask the question, *What is the sum of 2 and 3?* This is the same as saying *What is 2 plus 3 or 2 + 3?*

symbols

You use *symbols* in mathematics to name numbers (12, 308, $\frac{1}{2}$), operations ($+, -, \times, \div$), and relationships between numbers ($=, >, <$).